KOPTOE

Other Books by Ellen Palestrant

Nosedive
Johannesburg One Hundred
Remembering Dolores
Have You Ever Had a Hunch? The Importance of
Creative Thinking
I Touched a Star in My Dream Last Night
Pretzel on Prozac: The Story of an Immigrant Dog
The World of Glimpse
If You Can Make It, Mr. Harris…So Can I
If You Can Make It, Mr. Harris…So Can I Workbook
Let's Do Hunch

KOPTOE

TRANSCENDING BOUNDARIES: THE COMRADES MARATHON

Ellen Palestrant

epCreative Enterprises
www.EllenPalestrant.com

Library of Congress Control Number: To be assigned
ISBN: 978-0-9974783-3-4

Writing and illustrations
"JOGOTIC" has appeared in *I Touched a Star in My Dream Last Night* 1994, 2014
Koptoe has appeared in *Nosedive and Other Writings* 1983, *Harvest an Anthology* 1983

www.EllenPalestrant.com

Cover and Interior Layout: The Printed Page, Phoenix, AZ

Categories: Running & Jogging, Extreme Sports, Sports Training, Literature & Fiction, History, Politics, Writing, Creativity, Inspirational

To the memories of
Ad Donker and Lionel Abrahams,
two seminal figures
in South African Publishing and Literature.

Contents

You become what you think about all day long.
—*Ralph Waldo Emerson*

Nick: You know, Simon, if you want to run,
you have to be totally koptoe.
Simon: Yes...Always your mind is there.

JOGOTIC

Road Joggers on their morning run,
sprint for health, trot for fun.
Jog to be as fit-as-fiddles,
expand their chests; trim their middles.
Tilt on their heels, tip on their toes,
sprint in flimsy, running clothes.

Road joggers run in dreams at night:
silhouettes in darkness, shadows in moonlight.
On the road at dawn, they jog
till the end of day...
pounding paths of punishment,
until they fade away.

Can't give it up–they're too neurotic.
Run till they drop.
(Road Joggers are jogotic.)

Introduction to
KOPTOE

Introduction

*L*ife changes constantly; therefore, it is important to be adaptable, to think creatively and independently, and when necessary, to transcend seemingly insurmountable boundaries.

In my ongoing exploration of creative thinking, a subject I often write about, I examine the capacity of some people to push beyond what many — for a variety of reasons — perceive as entrenched, cast-in-stone limitations. Even though fearful of failure or of being thwarted at every turn, there are those self-challenging individuals who, driven by passion, optimism and courage, continue onwards against many odds.

Some years ago, I wrote a short story, KOPTOE (the title means "completely focused" in Afrikaans), about two South African runners, one black and one white, in training for and then participating in one of the most difficult marathons in the world — the 56-mile (89-90 kilometer) grueling Comrades Marathon — known as the world's oldest and largest ultramarathon. An ultramarathon is commonly defined as a footrace of fifty miles or more.

Both these men, Nick and Simon, were composites of a number of runners I knew — and also of some I had interviewed. Both men's vernacular and intonations, were *common to the times, a result of the many different cultural influences on South African English such as the nature of the multilingualism of the country, the imprints of tight-knit cliques, common interest groups, subcultures and shared experiences. All this, resulted in a lively colloquialism that continues to transform with the changing times.*

A few months before I wrote the story, I had begun to train for the Comrades Marathon of 1983 because my publisher, Ad Donker, knowing that I was a runner, suggested that we participate in the upcoming Comrades Marathon together. I started to train but then found that I did not have the time to commit to the demanding, all-consuming schedule involved, mainly because I was working on the television series, Johannesburg 100, *for the city's centenary. Instead, I wrote a story about two Comrade Marathon runners and their combined understanding of what is required to complete the race—a single-mindedness of purpose, enormously hard physical training, and a total commitment to reaching the goal. Ad Donker then added this story, KOPTOE, to my collection that he was about to publish* (Nosedive and Other Writings, *Published by Ad Donker/Publisher). He also included it in his* Anniversary Edition: Harvest—An Anthology. *Since then, KOPTOE has been performed a number of times as a monologue.*

I have now added additional chapters that follow after the actual story, to give some history of the Comrades Marathon and the politics of the times. I have also added chapters exploring some of the parallels between running marathons and the intense endeavors involved in writing and creating—also marathons in their own way. Of course, one could make similar comparisons with many professional disciplines and life itself; life is after all, an ultramegamarathon.

In order to aid those unfamiliar with some of the South African lingua franca, I begin—instead of end—with a short glossary…

—Ellen Palestrant

Glossary

Balaclava: used for cold weather and generally made of wool, it covers face and neck except for eyes and nostrils.

Gedoem: sound effect.

Graft: work.

Hele: *whole.*

Howzit: *a greeting—a combination of hello and how are you.*

Ja: yes.

Kaalgat: *naked.* Pronounced *karlgut.*

Kak*: excrement.*

Kip: *nap or sleep.*

Klomp*: clump.*

Kombi: *minivan.*

Koptoe*: a term that has been used in a number of ways, depending on context—head full: complete focus or head full of oneself.* Pronounced *koptoo.*

Lummies: *lumber jackets.*

Merc*: Mercedes.*

Oke: *guy.*

Panel-beaten: body-work

Pap: *corn porridge.*

Skaam*: embarrassment, shame.* Pronounced *skarm*

Vrekking: *dropping dead.*

Yessis/Yessus*: A form of "Jesus" as an exclamation.*

Background to Koptoe:

Progress is impossible without change, and those who cannot change their minds cannot change anything.
—George Bernard Shaw

Background to Koptoe

The Times and Setting:

The story takes place in 1983, thirty-five years after the Nationalist Party under Malan, first began to implement onto a South Africa already fairly segregated, a legal system of almost complete social, political and economic separation between the races in South Africa. The **Comrades Marathon**, founded in 1921, only opened its doors *officially* in 1975 to black contestants and to women.

The Scenes:

1. Johannesburg.

2. The grueling, uphill route of approximately fifty-six miles (89-90 kilometers) from the coastal city of Durban to Pietermaritzburg. Both cities are in the province of Kwazulu-Natal.

3. Johannesburg.

The Characters:

Nick—a white man, passionate about running, lives in a house in the suburbs of Johannesburg with his family.

Simon—a black man, also passionate about running, lives in the suburbs in the same room as his mother, Lettie, who lives in the backyard of her employers. Simon (like so many other people classified as non-white during those times) had to make do with whatever living quarters he could find. It was extremely difficult for non-whites to find legal accommodation in areas close to the cities as a result of the restrictions legislated by The Group Areas Act during the apartheid years. The only alternative people classified as non-white often had at the time, was to live in overcrowded areas and townships far from their work.

KOPTOE

PART ONE

I'm running well man. Totally *koptoe* with my running. I think of it all the time. Jeez, I'm really running well. I'm going to make the Comrades. I'm *going* to make it.

Hey—there's Simon. "Howzit Si. You're on the road early this morning. Did you manage *not* to wake your old lady this time?"

Simon's mother yells at him when he wakes her. I heard her once when I came to fetch him. You see, before a marathon, he usually waits on the pavement for us to pick him up. He's always right on time. We go together—me, Simon, Howard, who lives next door to me, and Jeffrey, who lives in Savoy. We usually go in Jeffrey's Merc because my car only sits two comfortably and Howard—well, he never likes to take his.

Anyway, one morning a few months ago, before the Stock Exchange Marathon, Simon was *not* waiting for us on the pavement as we had arranged, and so I had to go through the backyard to call him. I was careful though, not to wake the owners of the house, the Johnsons, whom I don't really know. Simon's mother, Lettie, works for them and Simon sleeps in her room in the Johnson's backyard. It's closer to his work. "One day I am going to have my *own* room, Nick," Simon told me once when we were running. "And my *own* house. I am going to make so much money for being famous from running."

Just as I was about to knock on Simon's window that morning when he wasn't waiting outside, his alarm went off real loud, causing his old lady to catch a fright. Jeez did she yell and Simon came running out of the room *kaalgat*, clutching his running clothes and shoes.

So now, seeing him run so early, I ask: "Hey Si, how did you manage to sneak out without waking your old lady?"

"I was really quiet this morning, Nick," he says. "I slept in my running clothes—always do nowadays. But not my shoes. Soon as I heard the alarm, I turned it off. Then I had a glass of water, took my shoes and crept out very quietly. And I never pulled the chain."

"Jeez! Is that all you have, Si—one glass of water before your run? Me—I have a tablespoon of yeast in orange juice for energy and a big spoon of molasses for iron, and two cups of coffee—strong and black, with two spoons of sugar in each cup to raise my blood-sugar. And a banana."

We're running up Campbell Street now and it's drizzling lightly. I tell you, there's nothing like running in the rain. Long as it's soft. I got caught in a hailstorm once—hand grenades they were. I kind of ran into them 'cause they weren't there one block before. It was bloody painful, I can tell you. They came smashing over my head and nose and back and arms and legs. I thought I'd have to be panel-beaten afterwards but I was all right.

I try to take no notice of the weather though when I run. Some mornings in winter, when it's very cold, I wear a balaclava and I cover my whole face except for my eyes because the air hurts my nose. As soon as I warm up, I take it off because it makes me all slobbery inside.

I'd rather run when it's cold than when it's hot. High humidity—that's the worst. I sweat a lot. Everything gets lost in my sweat. You've got to drink often when you run otherwise you can dehydrate. Happened to my mate Ernie during the Comrades last year. They had to put him on a drip. And he wasn't allowed to run for four weeks. Jeez! I'm always on the lookout for water taps.

"Nick," Simon says. "You eat too much before running. You're like Charlie Matlala. He takes two cups of coffee and brown bread—half. I don't know how he manages to run with half a loaf of bread in his stomach. I really don't understand how some guys do that. I run empty."

"Jeffrey has a plate of Muesli before he runs," I say. "It's good to have carbohydrates."

"But not in the morning," says Simon. "You must have it the night before."

We are running well together, Simon and me. We turn right at the top of Campbell Street and turn towards Oaklands. It's still drizzling. It's great! I like to run with Simon. He's fast and he's better than me. I don't mind. It's good training. Simon doesn't need to run with anyone, though. If you bump into him on the road, then he doesn't mind if you join him. But he never looks for people. Me—I like to talk when I run.

"So Si, your old lady doesn't like you to run?"

"No, she thinks I'm crazy. You know, one day she says to me: 'Simon, everyday you go out for nothing. For nothing! Sometimes, you come back with a little medal. What for? Afterwards, what are you going to get spending all your money on running? You don't bring back any money from it so what's the use?' So I said to her, 'When you've got running in your body, it's not easy to give up, Mom. Always, your mind is there.'"

He's right. Always your mind is there. Lisa says that's all I think about. Well, it's got to be like that. Totally koptoe with my running, I am. Totally koptoe.

"My mom, she thinks I'm crazy," Simon says. "Last Sunday, when it was raining hard, she says: 'Simon, must I make you a cup of tea?' and I said: 'No Mom, I'm going out for running. It's beautiful.' I love to run when it's raining. I can breathe.

"You know, Nick, my girlfriend was so cheeky till I started running. Always fighting with me. Not anymore. She respects me now. I've got so many friends these days. Everybody knows me."

Jeez, Simon runs well! He looks like he was born running. He's a natural. He can just wake up and run. Not like me. I've got a whole routine to get my vital organs in order, first. You should see me before a marathon: First, my alarm goes off an hour before Jeffrey fetches me. Then I get up and stretch for at least twenty-five minutes. I've got some great stretching exercises. Then I jog up and down the passage for about eight minutes. That helps to wake my leg muscles up. Then I spend another fifteen minutes under a lukewarm shower massaging all my back muscles. Then I get dressed, check my shoes to see there are no pressure areas or anything like that. Then I eat, do a few more stretches and wait outside for Jeffrey.

I never tell Simon I do all this beforehand. Actually, I don't tell any of the okes how hard I train. I tell them about the pain. That I do, 'cause everybody talks about the pain. You know, since I started running, I've suffered a lot. I've had Achilles tendinitis, heel-spur syndrome, runner's knee, shin splints—jeez, that was the worst. It's hard to describe. It's like somebody took a knife and put it under your shinbone. It's an inflammation of the lining of the shinbone. That's what it is.

"Hey Simon," I say. "You're lucky you don't have injuries from running."

"No," he says. "I have no trouble from running. Just from the girls. I'm not kidding, Nick. They all want me. I'm so famous, you know. Everyone sees me running. Before I started running, I never had friends. Now, when I catch the bus by the O.K., everybody greets me—guys and girls. Hey, which way do you want to go, Nick? Right or left?"

"Left," I say. It's drizzling still. Very lightly. I've got no pain. I'm running like a star. I'm running really well.

"You know, Si," I say, "I've got no more hassles with my knees. I do about twenty kilometers a day and they used to hurt after fifteen. I went to a special running doctor. He specializes in injuries. He put an orthotic into my shoe—it's like a flat wedge that fits into the shoe to build up the side of the heel. It's like magic. I have no pain anymore. Really. At first, I couldn't believe it. I tell you, that doc's a champ! Even from the bottom of my calves, the pain has gone. Hell man, to think a little wedge like that…Hey, Si…, what warming up exercises do you do?" I'm a bit short of breath now so I'll let Simon do most of the talking. Anyhow, I like to question him. Get a hint or two, you know.

"I touch my toes," he says, "twenty times before I run and twenty times after."

"That's all? You start off very slow, though?"

"Yes," he says. "If I run fast, I blow it."

"Still running to work every day?" I ask.

"Sure. My mother, she says: 'How can you wake up 5 o'clock in the morning and run to work twenty-two kilometers? How can you work properly in the bank?' I say, 'There's nothing I can do, Mom. I've got to go and run.' She thinks I'm crazy. When I come home with a medal, she wants to chuck it away and I say, 'No, Mom—it's better than anything. Keep that and maybe some day I'm going to show my kids. Maybe, they'll take up running. Maybe, one day when I'm seventy, I'll still be running and they'll say in the newspaper: *THERE'S SIMON, AND HE'S STILL RUNNING*. That's what I would like.'

"You should see my room, Nick. The wall above my bed is full of my medals and badges and certificates and pictures, all of running."

I also keep all my memories—that's what I call them—on the wall in our study and my green tracksuit is full of my badges that Lisa sewed on. Gregory—that's my kid—he's five, likes to count my badges. Come to think of it, I've accumulated a lot since I started running.

"How's your weight, Simon?" I ask.

"I'm down," he says. "I've cut everything I eat in half. Half pap. Half bread. Half meat. But you know Charlie Matlala, Nick—he's still taking a half a brown every morning and he's so thin. Man, have you seen how all those guys' bums have gone? They're running them off. How's your weight, Nick?"

"I'm down," I say.

You've got to keep your weight down. Lisa says every time I go to the bathroom, I get on the scale. It's true. Even if I go to the toilet at four in the morning, I get on it.

I tell you, I take my hat off to Simon. He's really koptoe with his running. You've got to be if you want to run well. Especially for the Comrades. Take me—from January the first, I started training. That means, by the time the Comrades comes, I will have done five months hard running just about every day of the week. I watch my diet all the time and never have late nights. 9:30—that's my limit. Even Saturdays. I reckon by the time I do the Comrades, I will have notched up two thousand, four hundred kilometers. How's that?

They say when you train, you should try to get all your muscles to graft. I read that you have six hundred and forty muscles in your body. Just imagine how long it would take to work them all!

"Do you know, Simon, a person has six hundred and forty muscles in his body? That's a lot of muscles. Let's say I exercise all of them every day. Spend half a minute on each one. That would take me six-hundred-and-forty half-minutes to do which adds up to three hundred and twenty minutes a day divided by sixty. Hell! Five hours! If I had to exercise all my muscles every day, it would take me five hours a day! Jeez! That would leave me no time for running. You know, Simon, if you want to run, you have to be totally koptoe."

"Yes," says Simon. We're running up Monroe Drive now. "Always your mind is there."

PART TWO

Drummond! Half-way. Boy! It's 10:45. That's okay. I've made Drummond in four hours and forty-five minutes. Not the greatest time, I know, but it's not like I have plans to go through the finishing post first or win a silver or bronze medal or anything like that. I just want to complete the Comrades in say nine hours and thirty minutes or ten hours thirty or ten hours forty-five—maximum. So long as it's less than eleven hours—that's the amount of time you are given to run ninety kilometers. Eleven hours and not a second more.

Ja, I'm making pretty good time. *Nick my mate, I'm proud of you. You're going to make it. No question. You've got what it takes, Nick, that's for sure. Jeez Nick, you can hold this pace forever.*

I'm talking to myself, I know. I often get like that when I do well or when I do something worthwhile—in my eyes. I become like unlinked. Unscrewed. Like suddenly there's two of me. Two parts. No—I'm explaining it all wrong. It's like I become two people—two *mes* but there's only one real me—the me who's watching the other me do something good. The real, *real* me watches and feels proud while the other me does the good. Like a father.

Nicky, you're dynamite. Look at you move man—like it's nothing. Like the top part of your body is catching a kip while your legs do all the graft. Like you're sitting back on sheepskins steering a Jag and the wheels go spinning along.

So you feel a bit of pain, Nick—so what? Forget it. It's nothing you can't handle. Hell man, you can take any punishment. You've done forty-five Ks, Nick. You're halfway and your feet are hardly touching the ground. Hey—don't think of the pain. Just cut off from it. From your shoulders down, you must feel nothing. Nothing Nick. Like Simon. Look at him. He feels no pain. Stick with him, Nick.

They reckon you should have a plan of action when you run the Comrades. You know that you've got eleven hours to get from Durban to Pietermaritzburg so you should work out in advance what time you should be at Westville Shopping Center for example and what time you should be at the top of Cowie's Hill and at the bottom of Field's Hill and Winston Park fly-over and Botha's Hill Hotel and so on. And then, of course, you must be at Drummond before eleven-thirty 'cause if you're not there in time, you're out of the race. You're not allowed to carry on 'cause you'll never make it.

I had a plan all worked out. Projections, you know, of times of arrival but when we set off and I saw Simon running in front of me, I thought: *Hell, why fuss all the way with your digital, Nick. Just follow Simon 'cause he's done the Comrades five times and last year, he made fantastic time—seven hours twenty-nine.* So I just locked in behind him and I've been running at his pace 'cause I know that even if he doesn't do his best time this year, he'll still make it. Guaranteed.

Ja, he'll definitely make it and during the last few Ks, if I see my time's not good, I can always increase my speed and just go for it.

I don't think Simon's even aware that I'm behind him. He's just running like he's in his own world. Just staring ahead. I spoke a bit to him in the beginning. I asked him how his training had been the past few weeks 'cause I hadn't bumped into him on the road.

He said, "Nick, my man, I've done a lot of mileage. It's beginning to hurt. You know, sometimes I've been feeling buggered but then, I put my mind together and I tell myself, *Simon, you've got to have a strong mind if you want to run fast. Let your legs work for you. Pick them up quick.*"

I ask him some more questions 'cause I like to talk when I run. It takes my mind off the pain but as we've gone along, he's got quieter and quieter. He's got this fixed stare like I said. So, I've quit trying to talk to him.

To tell you the truth, I'm finding it hard to talk myself. My pain is getting worse. I'm taking a lot of punishment. I've tried moaning and groaning out aloud. Saying "Ugh!" and "Ooh!" and "Yessus!" 'cause they say it takes extra energy *not* to show your pain. But I don't think it's working for me. It's making me even more aware of the pain.

It's better to switch off from the pain entirely. Think about something else. Like last night, for instance. What a carbo-party! We had a ball. There must have been twenty of us guys and some of their wives. Lisa and my kid, Gregory, came as well. They've come up to Durbs to watch the Comrades. Anyway, we met at a steakhouse and grazed chips and rolls and rice and pasta and milkshakes like they were going out of fashion. We grazed carbohydrates by the kilos 'cause we'd been on this Dr. Saltin's diet. He's an expert on nutrition for sports people. You start off by eating no carbohydrates whatsoever for three days. Just protein. No sugar. Nothing, and you continue your training. I can tell you, by the third day, all the guys on this diet were feeling shit 'cause carbohydrate is muscle food and the glycogen that you get out of it was all used up so we could hardly move our feet.

Then, on the fourth, fifth and sixth days, we had to cut out all the protein and eat only carbohydrates. Your muscles act like a sponge then and sop up all the carbohydrates they require for the run.

That's why, last night, we really binged on carbs 'cause if you're going to run 90 Ks, you're going to burn up a helluva lot of them. I went away feeling a bit stuffed up but that's the way the diet works.

Anyway, all the runners met at Durban City Hall early this morning. I was there by five-thirty and it wasn't even light yet 'cause May is winter. Even in Durbs. All the guys were stretching and warming up and the atmosphere was really tense.

And then at six, the gun went off—bang—and we all started running down Smith Street and the Berea and everything was steaming like crazy. You can imagine about five thousand bodies all sweating together 'cause everybody was bloody nervous.

It kind of reminded me of my rugby days at Highlands North High. Before a match, I would have the same nervous feeling that I experienced this morning waiting for the gun to go off. In those days, I used to pray that the guys we were going to play against, would not be too big. Hell, when we used to face one another on the field and size each other up, I sometimes found it hard to breathe but I always tried to make out I was confident. I'd stare down the biggest oke like he was Minnie Mouse and roll up my sleeves like I was a big deal. Jeez, I can remember those seconds before contact. They were the worst.

Anyway, this morning, we climbed all the way out of Durban. All the way. Shit, all the way. All the way up Field's Hill. All the way. Jeez, it was heavy going. Jeez, I'm hurting. *Hey Nick, you've got nothing to worry about. You're a star. Remember, you're doing the Comrades my mate—the ultimate marathon. Take a look at the scenery. Look at the dolly birds in their hot pants all lined up to cheer you on. They say at 'Maritzburg, all the nurses come out to watch you and they're great looking. Nick, look at the dollies.*

But I see nothing. Even if they were naked, I wouldn't see them. All I can think about is finishing. Going through that finishing post 'cause I'm hurting more and more. Jeez, I'm really, really hurting.

I drink a lot. At every refreshment station, I drink two cups of cold coke and water mixed together and I sponge often at sponging points. Ice-cold sponges. I have to leak a lot—about every two-and-a-half Ks. I'm watching my body. Everybody worries about their bodies. It's very important. So is the drinking. You must take in enough fluid.

Simon hardly stops to drink and I tell him he should, but he doesn't answer. He just runs. He's crazy, man. I don't care how fit you are, you've got to drink. He's not on form today but he knows the ropes. Hell, he's done the Comrades five times. He'll know when to put on the speed.

Jeez, I can't believe the silence. It's weird! Like uncanny, you know. I mean, there must be four hundred of us running together now and all you can hear is the silence. Ja—you can hear the silence and the feet—gedoem, gedoem, gedoem. And sweat.

This Polly Shorts is a killer. Hell, what a climb. I don't know if I can take anymore 'cause I'm hurting like crazy. It's four o'clock. Getting late but I can still make it. I'm pushing hard, Yessis, my lungs are burning and my body is sore. I'm paining everywhere.

Shit! What gives with Simon? He's stopped! He's clutching his calves and moaning. Jeez, what gives with Simon! He's lying on the road and shivering all over! Like he's having a fit and his legs keep shooting straight ahead. Jeez, what's happening with Simon! I don't want to stay with him. I've got no time but how can I go? "Go Nick. Go Nick. I'm not going to make it," he is saying but how can I go? I can't. I can't! "What's wrong, Simon," I'm asking but I know what's wrong. He's dehydrated. The idiot! The asshole! He's fucking dehydrated! And I'm stuck with him! Shit! I've got no time to stick around. "Go, Nick!" he says but I can't. I can't.

And then the St. John's guys come by and stop in their kombi and they take him in but I've wasted good time. Simon is crying. Crying like a baby and I also want to cry. Like a baby. Just like a baby.

I'm running and I want to cry 'cause I don't know if I'm going to make it. It's the pain and I can feel the tears building up. Funny, I'm no longer two Nicks. Just one screwed up Nick. One glued together with epoxy Nick. One real Nick who's going to cry in front of all these people. One born-loser Nick! And the pain! I'm going to burst apart because I want to howl and scream and yell! Try to think about something else, Nick. Try to think about something else.

Hey Nick—remember last year when you were play-ing snooker with Jeffrey and Howard? Do you remember? Remember how you had three Sprites—Super Sprites, one after another and you never burped once while you were playing? But afterwards, when you got to the foyer of the Carlton Hotel where Lisa was waiting, you felt it come up inside you and you tried to suppress it but you couldn't 'cause it was growing and growing and you couldn't control it and right there, in front of everybody, you let it out—the loudest burp ever heard anywhere—Uggh! Sounded like twenty horses neighing together in a cowboy movie when they were being attacked. Even louder. And everybody looked at you. Yessis—what a skaam!

What a skaam. I can't stop my tears and I can hear people shouting: "Go for it, Nick! Go for it!" I know why they know my name. It's because I've got my number on my vest and they've looked it up in their booklet. "Go for it, Nick! They shout like they really care. Like I'm their buddy. And there're some guys in black, leather lummies. Really raw okes and they're shouting: "Go for it, Nick! Go, go, go, Nick!" and I say, "Man, I've got nothing left inside me. I've got nothing to make it with," and I'm crying. Jeez, what a skaam.

I'm paining everywhere. I can't believe the punishment I'm taking. My whole body is sore but my calf feels like somebody is grabbing it and squeezing it every time I move and the left side of my knee is killing me.

Lisa says the worst pain anybody could experience is having a baby. Nothing could be worse than when she had Gregory. I thought the worst pain was when I came off my bike and dislocated my shoulder but I know better now. I tell you, I don't believe having a baby is one-tenth as bad 'cause I'm falling to pieces. It's like my body is going to break up all over the road and there's nothing holding my waist together. Nothing. My kneecap is falling off and my left foot— shit! My left foot is flopping. Just flopping along. I'm breaking apart man. I'm vrekking! I'm going to die!

I'm on the field and I can hear the guy shout: "Thirty seconds! Twenty-nine seconds!" But I can't make it. I'm on the field and I can see Lisa and Gregory hanging over the ropes watching out for me and I know I can't make it. My left foot is flopping along. Flopping along. Flopping. Fifteen seconds, fourteen seconds, ten seconds, five, four, three seconds and there's the gun and it's over. I haven't made it! Shit! I haven't made the Comrades 'cause I didn't go through the finishing post in time. I've achieved nothing. Nothing. I haven't made the Comrades.

Lisa is hugging me and I'm looking for Simon. He's not there. And I hear Gregory asking: "Why is Daddy crying?" and I start to shout, "'Cause it's all been for nothing! All for nothing. It's all been nothing but a hele klomp kak!"

PART THREE

I'm running well. Totally koptoe with my running. I'm going to make the Comrades this time 'cause I've learnt something. Hey—there's Simon. 'Howzit Si?" Like I was saying, I've learnt something. If you want to make the Comrades, you've got to be totally koptoe. You've got to really work hard. Be with me, you've got to do *one* year of solid training. No question.

Reflections on Koptoe

One thing I've found that I can do that I really enjoy is rereading my own writing, earlier stories and novels especially. It induces mental time travel, the same way certain songs you hear on the radio do… the whole thing returns, an eerie feeling.

—Philip K. Dick

I *wrote* KOPTOE *in 1983, a short story about two mara-thon runners, one a black man and the other white. I set this story against the backdrop of apartheid in South Africa and the Comrades Marathon, a roughly eighty-nine kilo-meter (about fifty-six mile) race. The Comrades Marathon is described today as the world's oldest and largest* ultra-marathon—*a footrace that is generally defined as being fifty miles or more.*

After not having looked at the story for many years, I recently read it again. I was struck by the parallels between the many marathons of our lives, and certainly the similarities between The Comrades Marathon *and our own* Life Marathons—*with the good, the difficult and the in-betweens. Much of the same qualities, such as fortitude and resilience, that marathon runners display as they climb steep hills and steel themselves against pun-ishing terrains, are required by us, too, as our journeys unfold and we adapt to changing circumstances. So many disciplines are personal* marathons, *too, from medicine, the sciences, establishing business enterprises, to different areas of sport, the arts—including music, dance, theater, film—all manner of demanding, rigorous pursuits.*

Other than my painting, most of my work contains a good deal of writing in various genres—fiction, poetry, film, and non-fiction. Much of my writing continues to be an exploration of creative thinking. My projects become marathons of varying lengths and endurance for me, espe-cially because I am compelled to complete what I begin as if I had signed a contract with myself.

My publisher, Ad Donker, knowing I was a runner at the time, suggested we run the Comrades Marathon together. Not very far into my training for the Comrades Marathon of 1983, I realized that I really did not have the time to commit to the huge preparation for the race. For once, I reneged on what I had committed to do, mainly because I was writing against a deadline at the time—a television series about the history of Johannesburg for the 1986 cen-tenary. So I transformed the early experiences I had from my training, the pre-research I had done, and the many conversations enjoyed with other runners, into the story, KOPTOE, because the possibility of running this race still resonated with me. I had decided to experience it through the invention of two men (composites of male runners with whom I had conversed) and to whose aspirations I could relate. I put myself into both their heads and running shoes.

Bringing ideas to fruition takes a huge amount of time and resolve. Running the Comrades also takes a huge amount of time and resolve. The road to completion is intense, focused and committed. A concept is not enough, just a beginning. Signing up for a running marathon is only a beginning; it is really about what comes after *that.*

For me, primarily as a writer, I see many parallels between running marathons and my own writing marathons.

Running Marathons and Writing Marathons

Runners Run,

Writers Write

&

Creators Create

Because That Is What They Do.

Similarities: An Overview

Both *running marathons* and *writing marathons* require intense focus, passion and a huge time commitment. Writing and completing a book, can take months or even years. The road from a creative concept to the final product is generally long, rocky and arduous; the road from *beginning* to train for the Comrades Marathon, and then actually *completing* it, is similarly grueling and punishing.

The similarities between running marathons and writing ones, became apparent to me when I read *KOPTOE* again—as did the similarities between completing large work endeavors (from books, to paintings, movies, scientific, educational, engineering, construction, and business projects) that require individuals to be committed for the long haul in order to bring what might have originally simply been a glimpse of possibility, to completion. All these major undertakings are marathons—and they are all about *finishing*.

The Commitment to Finishing

What does it take to be a finisher? Honoring a commitment for one, and also being self-challenging. People who are engaged in various forms of marathons throughout their lives, succeed because of their hard, hard work. They are the doers who are both purposeful and committed. They have the capacity to be completely focused. As Nick says in the story, *you've got to be totally **koptoe**…no question.*

Runners training for the Comrades Marathon, often follow self-devised, constantly improvised and self-imposed, preparatory programs. They build-up and tune-up all the time. It is hard work, sacrifice and pain. Quoting Nick again:

> *Do you know, Simon, a person has six hundred and forty muscles in his body? That's a lot of muscles. Let's say I exercise all of them every day. Spend half a minute on each one. That would take me six-hundred-and-forty half-minutes to do which adds up to three hundred and twenty minutes a day divided by sixty. Hell! Five hours! If I had to exercise all my muscles every day, it would take me five hours a day! Jeez! That would leave me no time for running.*

And to think that *all* that training, is not a guarantee of success—of completion. Yet runners, like writers, are propelled by that wonderful human condition called optimism, otherwise, without a positive outlook, they would not have begun to train in the first place. *Committed runners* try to run every day, despite any unpleasant weather conditions or physical pain; *committed writers* try to write everyday despite their pain of a different sort—the self-imposed captivity of sitting at a desk when they would rather go out to play in the glorious, beckoning weather. That is what is required to create a tangible, living, communicable book from what would otherwise have remained a small or large stack of paper in a folder, on a desk, in a drawer, or on a word processor, replete with unrealized potential. And as for running, a *marathon-not-run*, because a runner had not entirely committed to the pre-marathon strenuous preparation and then, as a result, actually not completed the race, would simply be a beguiling thought not fully acted upon.

Hunches and Advice

Runners, like writers, are offered a great deal of advice on how to train for running a marathon, much of which is useful. The best answers, however, comes from within the runners themselves—from their *own hunches*, those intuitive feelings that some suggestions are right for them while others are not.

Selecting what they deem is workable and what is not, is a result of both past experience and intuition—that feeling of confidence that goes beyond logic or analysis. Runners simply know, automatically, what is workable for them and what is not—as writers do—a result, too, of past experience—perhaps after having written thousands of words, and also, as a result of trusting their own intuitions.

Having the confidence and ability to trust their own hunches, can be a very useful mode of selecting from the abundant, well-meaning and often excellent suggestions of others. The more marathons runners run, the more they know; the more books writers complete, the more secure they become with their own writing processes.

Transcending Boundaries and the Long Haul

People who complete what they have set out to do, have to be self-challenging: ten pages today, twenty tomorrow, ten miles today, twenty tomorrow, a thousand miles in a year, and who knows how many in ten years. The road to completion is all about the long haul. The uphill, eighty-nine kilometer road from Durban to Pietermaritzburg is a foreboding climb: up Cowies Hill, up Fields Hill, Botha's Hill, Inchanga—all the way up Polly Shorts, the steep hill on the outskirts of the runners' *uprun* destination: Pietermaritzburg. The road to completing a book is also a long, one-paragraph-at-a-time, *uphill* haul.

Simon and Nick transcended physical boundaries, but in Simon's case, he transcended the major ones of the apartheid years—manmade barriers which barred him from much of life's opportunities: housing, education—equality. Both his passion and belief in self, as well as his commitment to draw from all the resources within himself that he could muster, helped him transcend not only his own physical boundaries, but the political ones of those times as well.

Purpose and Joy

Writing, like running a marathon, is a race against oneself, with imposed and self-imposed deadlines to be met and honored over weeks, months and years. The sacrifice goes with the doing—writing or running when you don't feel like it or are tired, writing and running instead of sleeping late on Sunday mornings, are all part of what finishers do—of what writers and runners do—because, really, they *want* to and they *have* to. It is their purpose. It beckons strongly at all times. The joy of the activity transcends the pain and sacrifice.

Nick: *You know, since I started running, I've suffered a lot. I've had Achilles tendinitis, heel-spur syndrome, runner's knee, shin splints—jeez, that was the worst. It's hard to describe. It's like somebody took a knife and put it under your shinbone. It's an inflammation of the lining of the shinbone. That's what it is.*

Long-distance running, just like many other physical, creative and work-passions, comes with a grim discipline and single-mindedness of purpose—an enduring belief in what one is hoping to achieve. Yes, it comes with sacrifice and much pain but then real life is seldom pain-free. For runners, however, pain becomes a distant and not-to-be-focused-upon backdrop. Runners have to run—and they have to be totally koptoe.

Nick (talking to himself): *So you feel a bit of pain, Nick—so what? Forget it. It's nothing you can't handle... Hey—don't think of the pain. Just cut off from it.*

There is joy in running, too—the headiness and the feelings of total exhilaration—similar to what is experienced when you are in the flow of the creative process. You don't want to stop. You feel you can go on forever.

Anticipatory Excitement and Self-Challenge

First, for runners, is the anticipatory excitement when they decide to commit to a marathon. There is a desire to do the necessary training despite the knowledge of the work that lies ahead. For writers, there are similar accompanying feelings of joy, expectation and optimism at the outset of a new creative project. What is the idea going to *become*?

The full engagement in the creative process can be exhilarating—and fun. The act of running, like creating, replenishes the spirits of runners and writers and that *glimpse of possibility* that they might succeed, or the desire to up the ante, achieving a better completion time than in past years, can be heady. There is no place for self-doubt. It's all about the process.

Like writers, marathon runners need to be self-directed, self-motivated and self-actualizing as they attempt to reach their running potential. The running path—like many work and life paths, is seldom easy. As Benjamin Franklin said two hundred years ago, there is "no gain without pain."

Solitude

Distance running, like writing, is a solitary path with much time spent alone. Fear of solitude would be an immense obstacle to doing distance running. Runners have to be comfortable with being alone with themselves and their thoughts. Aloneness allows for a good deal of thinking time—not always easy—and valuable opportunities to commune with themselves.

The Possibility of Failure

Finally, there is always the possibility of failing to complete the marathon, despite having put in so many months of training. It is the same with writing.

What a writer has worked on for months, just might not work as a book. He or she might have to start from the beginning again or even, give up on that particular theme—and that is never easy. Usually though, they work on what they have done, fleshing it out, editing it and molding it, until it reaches a form that satisfies them.

The Writing, Creating and Running Life

So *writers write, creators create, and runners run* because that is what they do. All are strongly beckoning purposes that guide them through years of practice and contemplation. This is what I see with so many people in the various areas of creativity with whom I am involved. The joy of the activity and the possibilities of succeeding, transcend the pain and sacrifice. What they do, is central to their lives and often for some, it is their life. They are committed…

Why Do Creators Create
and Runners Run?

1. *Creators Transcend Boundaries. Runners Transcend Boundaries.*

2. *Creators Create* in order to enrich their lives and in so doing, the lives of others. *Runners Run* in order to enrich their lives and in so doing, their example enriches the lives of others.

3. *A Life Devoid of Creativity* is barren for both individuals and society. *A Life Devoid of Running* can be a deprivation for the runner and for those who support the sport.

4. *Creators Create* in order to know what lies buried within them and to be elated with what emerges. **Runners Run** in order to know how much physical and emotional potential lies within them and to be elated with what they discover.

5. *Creators Create* because they are moved to do so. **Runners Run** because they are moved to do so.

6. *Creators Create* because they have the courage to do so. *Runners Run* because they have the courage to do so.

7. *Creators Create* because they have to do so—they just have to! *Runners Run* because they have to do so—they just have to!

8. *The Creative Life* offers the challenge of finding the answers from within and not only from external sources. *The Running Life* offers the challenge of finding the answers from within and not only from external sources.

9. *Creating can be Fun,* joyful and positive. *Running can be Fun,* joyful and positive.

10. *Creativity can be a Companion* for life. *Running can be a Companion* for life.

11. *Creators are Self-sufficient. Runners are Self-sufficient.*

12. *Creators Engage* in processes that require endurance. *Runners Engage* in processes that require endurance.

13. *Creators have the Habit* of overreaching. *Runners have the Habit* of overreaching.

14. *Creators Practice* intensely. *Runners Practice* intensely.

15. *Creators Focus* with intensity. *Runners Focus* with intensity.

16. *Creators Extend* themselves under pressure. *Runners Extend* themselves under pressure.

17. *Creators Experience* the flow when they are engaged in what they do. *Runners Experience* the flow when they are engaged in what they do.

18. *Creators Make* things happen for themselves. *Runners Make* things happen for themselves.

19. *Self-Motivation* is a major part of the psychological make-up of a creator. *Self-Motivation* is a major part of the psychological make-up of a runner.

20. *Creators* seldom give up. *Runners* seldom give up.

21. *Creators Constantly* up the ante for themselves. *Runners Constantly* up the ante for themselves.

22. *Creators are in Tune* with other creators. *Runners are in Tune* with other runners.

23. *Creators are Self-challenging. Runners are Self-challenging.*

24. *Creators are Passionate* about what they do. *Runners are Passionate* about what they do.

25. *Creators are Conscientious* about practicing. *Runners are Conscientious* about practicing.

26. *What Creators Choose to Do,* has to be meaningful to them. *What Runners Choose to Do,* has to be meaningful to them.

27. *The Lives of Creators* are purpose-driven. *The Lives of Runners* are purpose-driven.

28. *Creators are Resilient*—if they fail, they try again. *Runners are Resilient*—if they fail, they try again.

29. *Creating is addicting. Running is addicting.*

30. *Creators Create Goals* and push themselves to reach the finishing line. *Runners Create Goals* and push themselves to reach the finishing line.

The Comrades Marathon: Some Historical Background

There are many excellent books available on the subject of the Comrades Marathon as well as articles online for your further research. What follows, is a brief background about the history of the race and the political times for those who might not be acquainted with backdrop to my story, KOPTOE. The aspirations and achievements of these competitors are stories in their own rights and fortunately, many narrative accounts have been written about these contestants—many of whom won multiple races with completion times that often broke established records.

It began with a dream...

Dreams occur not only when we are asleep, they occur too, in our conscious minds and can be potent indications of what we really want. Daydreams are our visions, hopes and rehearsals for life. They direct us to what we would really like to achieve—if we pay attention to them. One man, Vic Clapham, was a dreamer and he did pay attention to his yearnings by initiating, and subsequently establishing what would one day become, an internationally renowned, athletic world-theater in which people from all walks of life would arrive with their dreams of competing in, finishing or even winning the **Comrades Marathon**. Over these many years, dreamers have entered this theater and have performed with remarkable prowess.

A Dream that Coursed through History

The Comrades Marathon today, is a giant international event, but it coursed through times when many contestants were kept out of the race—both women and those classified as *non-white*. A legislated practice of almost complete separation of races, ethnic groups and language speakers, had lead to the enforced separation of South Africans, despite their commonalities, their shared dreams and passions in so many areas—running the Comrades Marathon being one such example.

The first Comrades Marathon race was held on May 24th 1921, Empire Day—nearly one hundred years ago. Tumultuous years had preceded the establishment of what would be described as the world's oldest and most famous marathon, one that has endured and flourished despite a backdrop of immense socio-political upheaval and changes. This marathon was born out of war—and out of the dreams of one man—Vic Clapham who wanted to build a living memorial to those who had lost their lives. He also had a desire to memorialize the remarkable spirit of camaraderie among soldiers that he had personally witnessed in a lasting tribute, not only to them, but also, as a memorial for their families and the public.

South Africa had endured two wars in the twenty-one years before the Comrades Marathon was founded. First, there was the war between the Boers and the British—the Boer War—that lasted for two and a half years and ended on May 31st 1902 with the signing of the Peace of Vereeniging. This war had been devastating for both the British and the Boers. The loss of life and human suffering had been immense and tragic. The British had fought to secure their position in South Africa and the Boers had fought to retain their independence.

Thousands of black men were enrolled and both sides used many of them as combatants, drivers, guides and laborers. Thousands of black enrollees, as well as British and Boer combatants died. Thousands more were wounded. And then there were the deaths of Boer and Black civilians in separate concentration camps that numbered in the thousands because of poor sanitation, overcrowding and inadequate provisions.

According to Michael and Elize Mansvelt, in their article, *Et Tu Britannia* (**THE CLASS OF 1955 AND**

I, by Maurice Kahn, 2016) in the Boer concentration camps, "Mostly women and children died at the hands of the British—three thousand in Betulie and two thousand in Bloemfontein. There's a memorial list in the museum (in Bloemfontein) which goes on and on, seemingly without end. Thirty two thousand names, mostly women and children."

The Boer War had been bitter and tragic, yet only eight years later, South Africa became the latest dominion of the British Empire on May 31, 1910. For the non-white populations, it meant that now whites were constitutionally in control of the country.

Four years later, in August 1914, South Africa was once more at war but on the side of the British against the Germans…

World War One, triggered by the assassination of Franz Ferdinand, heir to the Austro-Hungarian throne in Sarajevo, Bosnia, was a global conflict (July 28, 1914–November 11, 1918). The war raged over locations in Europe, the Middle East, Pacific Islands, China, the coast of North and South America and also, Africa. When the armistice was signed in 1918, formally ending the First World War, the death and injury toll was horrifying—close to ten million killed, approximately nineteen and a half million wounded and six and a half million taken prisoner or missing. The tragedy and suffering was enormous.

Many South Africans had been reluctant to enter the First World War. They had not forgiven the English for the concentration camps and were thus opposed to going into war on the side of Britain against Germany, the latter country having aided them during the Boer War, but the Prime Minister of the Union of South Africa, Louis Botha, and his Minister of Defense, Jan Christian Smuts, conceded to a request by the British Government to invade German South West Africa. Smuts urged: "England has treated us well, given us back our liberty, and now she needs help." Then in 1919, South Africa was a signatory to the Peace Treaty of Versailles even though both Botha and Smuts had been perturbed by the harshness of the terms of the treaty.

Although the six thousand miles that separated South Africa from Europe also shielded her from the destruction of the war, there was still an intense awareness of the tragedy of it all. Over 146,000 combatants enlisted in South African units during this war, fighting in South-West Africa, France, and East Africa, with over 3000 South Africans joining the Royal Flying Corps. The casualties from many countries was horrifying: Over nine million combatants and seven million civilian died—and the total amount of South African casualties was 18,600—more than 6,600 of these, died.

This is the devastating war from which Vic Clapham emerged and from which the Comrades Marathon would indirectly originate. Vic Clapham had seen his friends and comrades endure terrible suffering during the war. So many had died or been severely injured. He had witnessed utter devastation. But he had also witnessed a remarkable togetherness even during the most horrifying of circumstances. He had observed an extraordinary spirit of camaraderie and was moved to honor those shared, empathetic emotions in some physical form that encapsulated comradeship in the face of all physical and emotional odds. He wanted to achieve this in the most enduring and significant way possible. And he did, in a deeply meaningful conception—the establishment of an annual Comrades Marathon race.

Vic Clapham, indeed, had devised a consequential, physically expressive way of saluting the soldiers who had undergone grueling, physical hardships, and embraced the strength of companionship in the face of horror. This was the enduring tribute he felt would be appropriate to their memory. This is how he wanted to honor the soldiers who had fallen and the ones who had survived—and all their families as well.

So Vic Clapham set out to pursue his vision by establishing an ultramarathon of roughly 89 kilometers —about 56 miles. The genesis for his idea had possibly been a walk already taking place from London to Brighton of a similar distance, one that had been undertaken quite regularly in the 1800s. The first authenticated such walk, occurred in 1897, and the Surrey Walking Club promoted it as early as 1902, going on to organize the first official race of 53 miles, starting at 6 a.m. at Westminster—within the chimes of Big Ben—and finishing at the Esplanade in Brighton.

Vic Clapham also selected two Natal towns of a similar distance apart for the race that he wished to establish for an annual event: *Pietermaritzburg and Durban*. Fully aware that former infantrymen, like himself, had managed to endure marches over huge distances and inhospitable terrain, he felt that these war veterans would be able to cover the 56-mile distance between these two towns.

Unable to find sufficient support from the athletic authorities of the time with whom he had consulted, he approached an existing association of South African former soldiers in 1918—the *League of Comrades of the Great War,* which had been formed in order to aid families impacted by their losses during the war. The League also wanted to cultivate opportunities for comrades who had survived and to provide them with camaraderie. Vic Clapham asked the League for permission to establish this marathon.

The organization, however, turned down the idea because they regarded the race as being too strenuous—even though these men who Clapham had in mind to run the first race, had marched hundreds of kilometers during their years of service. Clapham understood the physical endurance required for such a marathon, because he, himself, had signed up with the 8th South African Infantry and been sent to East Africa during the war. He had marched over 2700 kilometers in pursuit of the commander of the Imperial Army's German East African Campaign—General Paul Emil von Lettow-Vorbeck's and his Askari (local) battalions—a formidable force that had held in check the much larger forces that consisted of British, Belgian and Portuguese troops.

Vic Clapham again asked permission of the League in 1919 to establish the commemorative marathon and was again turned down, perhaps, because at the time, health was a major concern in South Africa and worldwide. During 1918 and 1919, there had been the outbreak of an international influenza pandemic—the Spanish 'Flu and commensurate feelings of fear and vulnerability, prevailed.

The Spanish Flu had caused the death of 50 million people throughout the world and the First World War had contributed to its rapid spread. Returning soldiers were malnourished and susceptible to the infection. The Flu had first arrived in South Africa through the port of Durban and then spread to the Witwatersrand. A second wave of infection, arrived from Cape Town Harbor and spread to the rest of the Cape, the Orange Free State and the Western Transvaal. Thousands in South Africa had become infected—and thousands died. The South African economy and the mining industry had been brought to a virtual standstill. The newspapers carried accounts of deaths. All manner of advice was proffered. Publications warned of symptoms:

> *Chilliness, sneezing, nasal discharge, intense pains in the head, chest ad back, cold perspiration, cough, expectoration, prostration, sometimes nervous manifestations, an increase of pulse and temperature, burning sensations in the eyes, and frequent nosebleeding.*

Remedies were recommended:

> *Remain for half an hour in water as hot as you can stand it. The water should be kept running so that the heat can be maintained. While in the tub*

drink about a quart of lemonade, so hot that you will have to sip it slowly.

Take one pound of lard, two teaspoons of turpentine, two of ammonia and one cake of gum camphor. Put in a pan on stove and heat. Wring flannel cloth out of mixture and apply to chest and back as hot as you can stand it. Take laxative.

Finally, in 1921, the League of Comrades of the Great War granted Vic Clapham permission to hold the event…

The first Comrades Marathon took place on May 24th, 1921, Empire Day. It started in rugged, hilly Pietermaritzburg in the Natal Province, called today, the Kwazulu-Natal province. It ended after a downhill race of 89 kilometers, in Durban—a subtropical port city on the eastern seaboard of Africa. The starting time for the first race was 7 am and the time limit was 12 hours.

Forty-eight runners entered the 1921 race but only thirty-four actually participated, many infantrymen from the Great War who had served in West Africa. Sixteen runners completed the race, Vic Clapham being one of them. Little did he know then that ninety-five years later, May 29, 2016, nearly 23,000 runners would participate in the Pietermaritzburg to Durban Comrades Marathon. Vic Clapham's dreams did take flight, even if at first, the start was slow.

The 1921 Comrades Down Race— PIETERMARITZBURG TO DURBAN:

MEN WINNERS–1921:

1st Place–Bill Rowan–8:59–
he was given a silver medal.
2nd Place–Harry Phillips–9:40
3rd Place–John A. Annan–10:10

1922 had 114 entries—**Uphill from DURBAN TO PIETERMARITZBURG**. The starting time was 6 am so that the last of the runners would reach the finishing post within the twelve-hour limit—that is before the winter dark set in.

MEN WINNERS–1922:

1st Place–Arthur Newton–8:40
2nd Place–Harry Phillips–9:09
3rd Place–Bill Rowan–9:13

1923—an *unofficial* contestant for the **Downhill— PIETERMARITZBURG TO DURBAN RACE—A WOMAN:** *Frances Haywood,* who was refused entry as an official contestant.

Frances Haywood ran nevertheless, and completed the race in *eleven hours and thirty-five minutes—* well within the twelve-hour cut-off point that had been instituted, plus she finished in the 28th place.

However, she was not awarded a Comrades Medal. Other runners and spectators did bestow on her a *silver tea service and a rose bowl.*

MEN WINNERS–1923:

1st Place–Arthur Newton–6:56
2nd Place–N. Nel–7:48
3rd Place–A. Purcell–8:17

1924 race—Uphill DURBAN TO PIETER-MARITZBURG only had 31 entrees:

MEN WINNERS–1924:

1st Place–Arthur Newton–6:58
2nd Place–G. Shackleford 8:13
3rd Place–C. Strasburg–8:48

The 1920s was the age of jazz and much heady physicality—*The Tango, The Bunny Hug, The Charleston, The Turkey Trot, and now, The Comrades Marathon*—born, also, in the age of electricity—electric lighting, stoves, toasters, kettles, irons, fridges, even waffle-makers, the first traffic lights, huge leaps in modernization. And then, there was the Wall Street Crash in 1929: Millions of people in Europe and in America were economically ruined. The climate reverberated in South Africa, and the country, too, plunged into a depression felt by nearly every industry, particularly when, in 1931, Britain abandoned the gold standard to which South Africa was linked—but then, South Africa abandoned the gold standard, too, and a boom started soon after that.

And over that period of ten years, from when the Comrades Marathon, was first established, the race, too, had its booms and plateaus:

1925—Down Race: PIETERMARITZBURG TO DURBAN:

MEN WINNERS—1925:

1st Place–Arthur Newton–6:24
2nd Place–Harry Phillips–7:05
3rd Place–G. Shackleford 7:17

1926—Up Race—DURBAN TO PIETERMARITZBURG:

MEN WINNERS—1926:

1st Place–Harry Phillips–6:57
2nd Place–Arthur Newton–7:02
3rd Place–Frank Sutton–8:09

1927—Down Race—PIETERMARITZBURG TO DURBAN:

MEN WINNERS 1927:

1st Place–Arthur Newton–6:40
2nd Place–Frank Sutton–7:15
3rd Place–W. Sutton–7:52

1928—Up Race—DURBAN TO PIETERMARITZBURG:

MEN WINNERS–1928:

1st Place–Frank Sutton–7:49
2nd Place–R. Sutton–7:57
3rd Place–F. Hendriksen–8:19

1929—Down Race—PIETERMARITZBURG TO DURBAN:

MEN WINNERS–1929:

1st Place–Darrell Dale–7:52
2nd Place–W. Wallace–8:10
3rd Place–A. Marie–8:17

1930—Up Race—DURBAN TO PIETERMARITZBURG:

MEN WINNERS–1930:

1st Place–Wally Hayward–7:27
2nd Place–Phil Masterson-Smith–7:28
3rd Place–CF. Munnery–7:39

1931—Down Race—PIETERMARITZBURG TO DURBAN:

MEN WINNERS–1931:

1st Place–Phil Masterson-Smith–7:16
2nd Place–N.C. Burree–7:16 (really a tie)
3rd Place–W. Strydom–7:32

And a woman entree as well—*unofficially*: **Geraldine Watson** ran unofficially in 1931 and in 1932. She finished just before the 12 hours were up.

In 1933, she completed the run in 9:31:25.

The first nineteen years following the establishment of the Comrades Marathon in South Africa, were relatively peaceful, but the peace was all too soon shattered when in 1938, Hitler annexed Austria and Germany and in 1939, attacked Poland. Britain and France declared war on Germany. And in South Africa, there was serious division within the cabinet on the question of where it stood with regard to the war. General Hertzog's policy of friendship with Germany was rejected in favor of Smut's declaration of the country's place at the side of Great Britain. Hertzog resigned. General Smuts became prime minister and minister of defense, and later, commander-in-chief of the armed forces.

Far from major battle lines, safe from invasion, South Africa was nevertheless deeply involved in the Second World War. Many of her men had gone off to fight. General Smuts was committed to ejecting Italy from Abyssinia, the achievement of which he believed, was the responsibility of the Union of South Africa. He was convinced of the necessity of guarding the sea route around the Cape.

The forces required to realize this task, consisted largely of volunteers who had undergone a swift period of training. By the mid-1940s, the South African Air Force was in action in Abyssinia, followed at six-monthly intervals by the First and Second Infantry Division. Men were absent but work had to be done. Women were called into the workshops. Soon, under the supervision of mine artisans, they were helping in the manufacture of essential war supplies such as bombs, shells, guns, howitzers and field guns.

Against this war backdrop, the 1940 Comrades Marathon took place despite the fact that South Africa was preparing for war. There were not many entries of course, but, when, on the actual night before the race, France and the Low Countries were invaded by Hitler and by the actual day of the Marathon, the Allied Armies had to retreat towards Dunkirk and the English Channel—the British Government having decided to evacuate the British Expeditionary Force as well as some French Divisions—a number of the participants withdrew their entries. They had decided to enlist.

The 1940 race from Durban to Pietermaritzburg (the last one until 1946 when the Comrades Marathon resumed again), *did* take place, however, with twenty-three athletes participating, and the winner, Alan Boyce, completing it in 6 hours and 39 minutes.

1940—Up Race—DURBAN TO PIETERMARITZBURG:

MEN WINNERS—1940:

1st Place–Alan Boyce–6:39
2nd Place–W.D. Parr–8:29
3rd Place–G.G. Morrison–8:55

However, between the years 1941 and 1945, no Comrade Marathon races were run. **The world was at war.**

On May 7, at 2:41 a.m., the German surrender took place in a red schoolhouse in Rheims—at the Headquarters of Allied Supreme Commander, General Eisenhower. Hostilities in Europe ended officially at midnight, May 8, 1945. Prime Minister Winston Churchill broadcast: *Yesterday morning at 2:41 a.m. (May 7, 1945) at Headquarters, General Jodl, the, the representative of the German High Command, and Grand Admiral Doenitz, the designated head of the German State, signed the act of unconditional surrender of all German Land, sea and air forces in Europe to the Allied Expeditionary Force, and simultaneously to the Soviet High Command...The German war is therefore at an end...Finally almost the whole world was combined against the evil-doers, who are now prostrate before us. Our gratitude to our splendid Allies goes forth from all our hearts in this Island and throughout the British Empire...We may allow ourselves a brief period of rejoicing; but let us not forget for a moment the toil and efforts that lie ahead...*

On May 8, 1945, Reich Minister Count Schwerin von Krosigh, broadcast to his people: *German men and women, the high commando of the armed forces has today, at the order of the Grand Admiral Doenitz, declared the unconditional surrender of all fighting German troops. After a heroic fight of almost six years of incomparable hardness, Germany has succumbed to the overwhelming power of her enemies.*

The biggest war in history had lasted for almost 6 years. 50 million people had been killed—15 million soldiers, millions of Russian, Polish and other civilians—and six million had Jews died. General Smuts congratulated his people on "a victory more colossal than we ever dreamed of and towards which South Africa has, according to her strength, contributed an unstinted measure." Winston Churchill paid tribute to "the magnificent war effort of South Africa as a whole under the leadership of Field Marshall Smuts."

The ever-present capacity for human resilience was evident as life resumed again in seemingly normal ways, despite the tragedy of the immense loss of human life. The Comrades Marathon also resumed again but the emotions of loss—the deaths of previous participants and winners killed in action— Phil Masterson-Smith and Frank Sutton, was sadly acknowledged. Frank Sutton had come in 3rd in 1926, 2nd in 1927, and 1st in 1928, while Phil Masterson had come in 2nd in 1930 and 1st in 1931.

However, in 1946, the Comrades Marathon commenced its annual races and twenty-two contestants participated. The last race in 1940 had been an up race and the 1946 race was an up one as well:

1946—Up Race—DURBAN TO PIETERMARITZBURG:

MEN WINNERS–1946:

1st Place–W.J. Cochrine–7:02
2nd Place–W.D. Parr–8:00
3rd Place–W.A.C. Rufus–8:27

Nineteen forty-eight was a dramatic year in the life of Johannesburg: General Smuts and his ruling United Party were toppled in the general elections of the tenth Union parliament. The Nationalist Party, which had been founded in 1915, now succeeded with Dr. Daniel Francois Malan as Prime Minister. Their victory had been unexpected and the margin by which they won, thin, but, immediately, the Nationalist Party began to implement a system of apartheid—separateness— specifically designed to guarantee white domination and survival. There had been segregation before the Nationalists came into power in 1948, but now it was instituted along the entire length and breadth of race relations.

Once firmly in power, the Nationalist Party under the leadership of D.F. Malan, began to implement a legal system of complete economic, social and political separation between the races.

On the second day of Spring of that year, September 2nd, the report of the Nationalist Party's

Commission on apartheid, published a few months previously in The Star, appeared:

The principle of territorial segregation between whites and natives is in general accepted. The party undertakes to protect the white character of the towns. The natives in our town must be regarded as a visitor with no claims to political rights there. The number of detribalized natives is to be frozen. Movements of natives to town must be controlled by the State.

Black people had become *temporary sojourners* in white cities where they needed to work. They would have to return at night after work, to accommodations in overcrowded townships. Race laws continued to be implemented and these added further to the deprivations of those deemed and classified not to be privileged. *A Population Registration Act* was passed by which people were placed into categories of race, the major divisions being *white, black* and *colored*. And then there was further subdivision of categories: *Cape Malay, Cape Colored, Chinese, Indian, Griqua, other Asiatics and Colored.* Bureaucrats were kept busy and many wielded power over others. Essentially, this was a totalitarian regime.

Separate living areas for each race was legislated in the *Group Areas Act* and people were forcibly removed from the areas in which they had been living. Many acts were passed including *The Job Reservation Act* in 1948 that mandated that only white people could perform skilled labor. There was inequality in wages, living conditions, educational opportunities, athletic opportunities—in all manner of personal growth and human rights. This was still going on in the 1970s:

A law was passed in 1974—*The Afrikaans Medium Decree*—instituting that all black schools had to be taught in Afrikaans *fifty percent* of the time and the other *fifty percent*, in English. Also, certain subjects such as mathematics and social sciences, had to be taught only in Afrikaans. The problem was that many black children did not speak Afrikaans so that added tremendously to their disadvantages. The required textbooks for these students, had to be published in Afrikaans as well, making studying even more difficult for them.

International protests against apartheid increased. These protests affected sport as well. In 1970, the member nations of the International Cricket Conference, suspended South Africa indefinitely from international cricket competitions and the South African's Cricket Board's application for readmission was refused again in 1974. The British Lions Rugby did tour South Africa in 1974, however, beating the Springboks in twenty-one of the twenty-two matches.

That year also, the uphill Comrades Marathon of 1974 took place. It was still open *only to white men:*

MEN WINNERS–1974:

1st Place–Derek Preiss–6:02
2nd Place–J. Sutherland–6:04
3rd Place–Alan Robb–6:06

There had been some shifts towards integration during that period though, including in sports. By 1974 and the latter half of that decade, there was an opening up for many athletes who were not white. In1975, **The Golden Jubilee, of Comrades**, brought sorely needed transformations to the Comrades Marathon. Doors were finally opened to both women and to all race groups. The pool of talent grew enormously. The uphill race that year, had a female winner:

MEN WINNERS–1975:

1st Place–Derek Preiss–5:53
2nd Place–G.W. Shaw–6:03
3rd Place–J. Sutherland 6:06

A WOMAN WINNER–1975:

1st Elizabeth (Bettie) Cavanagh–10:08

By 1975, the Comrades had metamorphosed into a national annual event and although still under international sport sanctions which were not to be lifted until 1993, an ever-increasing amount of runners from all over the world had started to compete in the annual event. There had been unofficial black runners in the past—as far back as 1935 when Robert Mtshali had completed the race and been given a small but separate presentation. Over the years, many more were to run *unofficially*, but in 1975, Vincent Rakabaele, now an *official* Comrades Marathon contester, was awarded a medal when he finished in 20th place in a time of 6 hours and 27 minutes. In ensuing years, he finished in 4th and 8th positions.

Women, too, had run—unofficially—as far back as 1923 when Frances Hayward had been refused official entry and had run unofficially. A Durban schoolteacher, Geraldine Watson, ran unofficially in 1931, 1932 and 1933. Mavis Hutchinson and Maureen Holland also ran unofficially in the 1960s completing many marathons. Lettie Van Zyl competed unofficially in 1973—and then went on to win *officially* in 1976, 1977 and 1978.

In January 1976, television came to South Africa— at last. TVI broadcast in English and Afrikaans on one channel. The Comrades Marathon was now widely covered by television.

The 1976—Downhill Race:

MEN WINNERS–1976:

1st Place–Alan Robb–5:40
2nd Place–C. Woodward–5:49
3rd Place–D.A. Rogers–5:52

> **WOMEN WINNERS–1976:**
>
> 1st Place Lettie Van Zyl–9:05
> 2nd Place–A. Kleynhans–9:35
> 3rd Place–L. Obelholzer–9:53

In June 1976, there were the Soweto riots, also covered by television. Unrest spread throughout the country. There were protests against discrimination, protests against using Afrikaans as a teaching medium for black children, and many now took to the streets. Violence and death spread to other townships. July 1976 saw the eviction of Indian traders from Pageview and their resistance to moving established businesses to the Oriental Plaza.

The Comrades Marathon continued through it all. Records were broken: Alan Robb in 1978 in an extraordinary 5:29.14—having done the up run from Pietermaritzburg and runner-up David Wright, 20 minutes behind him on this uphill race. The Comrades Marathon grew enormously during the 1980s. In 1977, for example, there had been 1,678 entries and in 1983, there were more than 5000.

The political turmoil, however, continued to mount. There was recession, retrenchments, disinvestment, world condemnation, isolation, unemployment, violence, confrontation, deadlock, emergency measures. Runners protested, too. Bruce Fordyce wore a black armband to signal his protest—and he won the race. In 1989, there was a black winner—Sam Tshabalala.

South Africa was changing dramatically and irrevocably. The Comrades Marathon, an institution that broke not only physical barriers but racial ones as well, continued to thrive through these changes. On February 2nd, 1990, the African National Congress was legalized, and Nelson Mandela was released after twenty-seven years in prison. In the same year, the Nationalist Party became open to all racial groups and began to repeal racial legislation that had been the foundation of apartheid. In 1993, the Nobel Peace Prize was jointly awarded to Nelson Mandela and F.W, de Klerk "for their work for the peaceful termination of the apartheid regime, and for laying the foundations for a new, democratic South Africa."

Elections were held in 1994 and were won by the African National Congress. The National Party, however, remained in government as a coalition partner to the ANC in a government of National Unity until June 1996, when it withdrew to become the official opposition.

In the 1990s, there were 12,000 to 14,000 competitors participating in the Comrades Marathon and in 1995, prize money was introduced. In the 2016 Comrades Marathon, more than 23,000 entrants from over 60 countries came to compete in the 89 kilometer (approximately 56 mile) up race. When the Marathon was first run in 1921, the cut-off time had been 12 hours. In 1928, it was changed to 11 hours and remained that until 2003, when it became 12 hours again.

Many medals have been won over the years by the contestants:

GOLD MEDALS

Awarded to the *first ten* men and women. This medal had initially been introduced in 1931 and given to the *first six* men to complete the race. Gold Medals were introduced for the *first* woman in 1983 and from 1988, to the *first three* women; in 1995, the *first five* women to finish the race. Then, in 1998, the *first ten* women to cross the finishing line, were awarded gold medals—the same as the men's event.

WALLY HAYWARD MEDAL

Introduced in 2007 and awarded to those who finish within 6-hours. It was named after the five-time winner, Wally Hayward, who was one of the greatest South African runners.

SILVER MEDAL

In 1931, it was awarded to *all* men who finished the race but since 1972, to runners finishing in *under seven hours thirty minutes*. From 1979 to 1981, a silver Medal was awarded to the *first* Woman winner.

BILL ROWAN MEDAL

Instit*uted in 2000, for runners achieving a time from 7 hours 30 minutes to* sub 9 hours. Bill Rowan won the 1921 race and finished in *eight hours and fifty-nine minutes.*

BRONZE MEDAL

Instituted in 1972 for those completing the race in *under 11 hours.* Bronze medals were first awarded to women in 1975.

VIC CLAPHAM MEDAL

Instituted in 2003, this copper medal, was named after the founder of the Comrades Marathon, Vic Clapham, who, in 1921, had completed the very first race he had founded. It was awarded to those finishing in *11 hours to sub 12 hours*. Additional time was now allocated for the completion of the Marathon—from the previous eleven hours to twelve hours.

BACK2BACK

Introduced in 2005, this was awarded to novices that complete an up and down run consecutively.

The Comrades Marathon is today, a major international annual event: Cash prizes were introduced in 1995 and the race became more commercial. By 1996, it became the biggest sport happening in South Africa.

1996 had its first Russian winner—Dmitri Gtishine (5:29.33). In 1999, there was a winner from Poland—Jaroslaw Jamicki (5:3) and in 2000, Vladimir Kotov of Belarus (5:25.33)—a new record. Maria Bak of Germany in 1995 came in first (6:22). In 2009, the winner was a runner from Zimbabwe—Stephen Muzhingi. He completed the run in five hours, twenty-three minutes and twenty-seven seconds. Stephen Muzhingi then won the down race the following year in 2010, with a time of 5:29:01 and then again on the uphill race, in 2011 (5:32.45)

How different it now was for women and black contestants! Frances Hayward had run unofficially in 1923, Geraldine Watson, unofficially, in 1931, 1932 and

1933. Then in 1965, Mavis Hutchinson had run unofficially, finishing in 10:07, Maureen Holland, unofficially in 1966 finishing 9:30, in 8:37 in 1971, in 9:26 in 1972 and in 8:40 in 1973. In 1971, Elizabeth Cavanagh had run unofficially and finished in 10:50, and in 10:08 in 1975—but by then, she was able to run *officially*. The doors were finally open to women and black contetants, who now finished in remarkable times.

In 1989, Frith van der Merwe completed the down race in 5:54:43. By 1994, there were international women winners of the Comrades marathon: Valentina Lyakhova from Russia won the women's up race in 1994 (6:41:23), Maria Bak of Germany won the Women's down race in 1995—again in 2000 and 2002, (6:22:57.) Ann Trason of the United States won the Women's race in 1997 (5:58:24), Birgit Lennartz of Germany in 1999 (6:31:03). Twin sisters, Elena and Olesya Nurgalieva from Russian won many of the races—Olesya won in 2007 and 2009, while her sister, Elena, won in 2003, 2004, 2006, 2008, 2010, 2011, 2012, and 2013—eight times in total! Eleanor Greenwood from the United Kingdom, won in 2014, while two South African women won in 2015—Caroline Wostmann and Charne Bosman.

The men's races, too, had become multi-racial and international—a far cry from its beginnings in 1921. The first Russian winner in 1996, was Dmitri Grishine (5:29:33). It is interesting to examine the first place winners from 1921 to 2016 with regard to both the ever-increasing diversity and the extraordinary physical abilities of the runners as they attempted to equal or beat existing records:

1921–down: Bill Rowan South Africa (8:59) *

1922–up: Bill Rowan South Africa (8:40) *

1923–down: Arthur Newton South Africa (6:56)*

1924: Arthur Newton S.A. (6:58:22)*

1925–down: Arthur Newton S.A. (6:24:45)*

1926–up: Harry Phillips S.A. (6:57:46)*

1927–down: Arthur. Newton S.A. (6:40)*

1928–up: Frank Sutton S.A.(7:49:07)*

1929–down: Darrell Dale S.A. (7:52:00)*

1930-up: Wally Hayward S.A. (7:27:26)*

1931–down: Phil Masterson-Smith S.A. (7:16:30)*

1932–up: William Savage S.A. (7:41:58)*

1933–down: Hardy Ballington S.A. (6:50:37)*

1934–up: Hardy Ballington S.A. (7:09:03)*

1935- down: Bill Cochrane 6:30:05)*

1936–up: Hardy Ballington S.A. (6:46:14)*

1937–down: Johnny Coleman S.A. (6:23:11)*

1938–up: Hardy Ballington S.A. (6:32:26)*

1939–down: Johnny Coleman S.A. (6:22:05)*

1940–up: Allen Boyce S.A. (6:39:23)*

1941–1945 (War–Comrade Marathon suspended)*

1946–up: Johnny Coleman S.A.(7:02:40)*

1947–down: Hardy Ballington S.A. (6:41:05)*

1948–up:William Savage S.A. (7:13:52)*

1949–down: Reg Allison S.A. (6:23:21)*

1950-up: Wally Hayward S.A.(6:46:25)*

1951–down:Wally Hayward S.A. (6:14:08)*

1952–up: Trevor Allen S.A. (7:00:02)*

1953–up:Wally Hayward S.A. (5:52:30)*

1954—up: Wally Hayward S.A. (6:12:55)*

1955—down: Gerald Walsh S.A. (6:06:32)*

1956—up: Gerald Walsh S.A. (6:33:35)*

1957—down: Mercer Davies S.A. (6:13:55)*

1958—up: Jack Mekler S.A. (6:26:26)*

1959—down: Trevor Allen S.A. (6:28:11)*

1960—up: Jack Mekler S.A. (5:56:32)*

1961—down: George Claasen S.A. (6:07:07)*

1962—up: John Smith United Kingdom (5:57:05)*

1963—down: Jack Mekler S.A. (5:51:20)*

1964 _- up: Jack Mekler S.A.(6:09:54)*

1965—down: Bernard Gomersall United Kingdom (5:51:09)*

1966—up: Tommy Malone S.A. (6:14:07)*

1967—down: Manie Kuhn S.A. (5:54:10)*

1968—up: Jack Mekler S.A. (6:01:11)*

1969—down: Dave Bagshaw S.A. (5:45:35)*

1970—up: Dave Bagshaw S.A. (5:51:27)*

1971 -down: Dave Bagshaw S.A. (5:47:06)*

1972—up: Mick Orton United Kingdom (5:48:57)*

1973—down: Dave Levick S.A. (5:39:09)*

1974—up: Derek Preiss S.A. (6:02:49)*

1975, The Golden Jubilee of the race, saw huge transformations in the tradition of the Comrades Marathon: the doors were finally flung open to both women and to blacks. The pool of talent was now enormous.

Men and Women (officially)

1975–up: men–Derek Preiss S.A.(5:53:00) women–Elizabeth Cavanagh S.A. (10:08:08)*

1976–down: men–Alan Robb S.A. (5:40:53) women–Lettie VanZyl S.A. (9:05:00)*

1977–up: men–Alan Robb S.A. (5:47:00) women–Lettie Van Zyl S.A. (8:58:00)*

1978–down: men–Alan Robb S.A. (5:29:14) women–Lettie Van Zyl S.A. (8:25.00)*

1979–up: men–Piet Vorster S.A. (5:45:02) women –Jan Mallen S.A. (8:22:41)*

1980–down: men–Alan Robb S.A. (5:38:25) women– Isavel Roche-Kelly S.A. (7:18:00)*

1981–up: men–Bruce Fordyce S.A. (5:37:28) women–Isavel Roche-Kelly S.A. (6:44:35)*

1982–down: men–Bruce Fordyce S.A. (5:34:22) women–Cheryl Winn S.A. (7:04:59)*

1983–up: men–Bruce Fordyce S.A. (5:30:12) women–Lindsay Weight S.A. (7:12:56)*

1984–down: men–Bruce Fordyce S.A. (5:27:18) women–Lindsay Weight S.A. (6:46:35)*

1985–up: men–Bruce Fordyce S.A. (5:37:01) women–Helen Lucre S.A. (6:53:24)*

1986–down: men–Bruce Fordyce S.A. (5:24:07) women–Helen Lucre S.A. (6:55:01)*

1987–up: men–Bruce Fordyce S.A. (5:37: 01) women–Helen Lucre S.A. (6:48:42)*

1988–up: men–Bruce Fordyce S.A. (5:27:42) women–Frith Van Der Merwe S.A. (6:32:56)*

1989–down: men–Samuel Tshabalala S.A. (5:35:51) women–Frith Van Der Merwe S.A. (5:54:43)*

1990–up: men–Bruce Fordyce S.A. (5:40:25) women–Naidene Harrison S.A. (7:02:00)*

1991–down: men–Nick Bester S.A. (5:40:53) women–Frith van der Merwe S.A. (6:08:19)*

1992–up: men–Jetman Msutu S.A. (5:46:11) women–Frances van Blerk S.A. (6:51:05)*

1993–down: men–Charly Doll Germany ((5:39:41) women–Tilda Tearle S.A. (6:55:07)*

1994–up: men–Alberto Salazar United States (5:38:39) women–Valentina Lyakhova Russia (6:41:23)*

1995–down: men–Shaun Meiklejohn South Africa (5:34:02) women–Maria Bak Germany (6:22:57)*

1996–up: men–Dmitri Grishine Russia (5:29:33) women–Ann Trason United States (6:13:23)*

1997–down: Charl Mattheus S.A. (5:28:37) Ann Trason United States (5:58:24)*

1998–up: men–Dmitri Grishine Russia ((5:26:25) women–Rae Bisschoff South Africa (6:38:57)*

1999–down: men–Jaroslaw Janicki Poland (5:30:10) women–Birgit Lennarte Germany (6:31:03)*

2000–up: men–Vladimir Kotov Belarus (5:25:33) women–Maria Bak Germany (6:15:35)*

2001–down: men–Andrew Kelehe South Africa (5:25:51) women–Elvira Kolpakova Russia (6:13:53)*

2002–up: men–Vladimir Kotov Belarus (5:30:59) women–Maria Bak Germany (6:14:21)*

2003–down: men–Fusi Nhlapo South Africa (5:28:52) women–Elena Nurgalieva Russia (6:07:46)*

2004–up: men–Vladimir Kotov Belarus ((5:31:22) women–Elena Nurgalieva Russia (6:11:15)*

2005–down: men–Sipho Ngomane S.A, (5:27:10) women–Tatyana Zhirkova Russia (5:58:50)*

2006–up: men–Oleg Kharitonov Russia (5:35:19) women–Elena Nurgalieva Russia (6:09:24)*

2007–down: men–Leonid Shvetsov Russia (5:20:49) women–Olesya Nurgalieva Russia (6:10:11)*

2008–up: men–Leonid Shvetsov Russia (5:24:49) women–Elena Nurgalieva Russia (6:14:38)*

2009–down: men–Stephen Muzhingi Zimbabwe (5:23:27) women–Olesya Nurgalieva Russia (6:12:08)*

2010–down: men–Stephen Muzhingi Zimbabwe (5:29:01) women–Elena Nurgalieva Russia (6:13:03)*

2011–up: men–Stephen Muzhingi Zimbabwe (5:32:41) women–Elena Nurgalieva Russia (6:24:11)*

2012–down: men–Ludwick Mamabolo South Africa (5:31:03) women–Elena Nurgalieva Russia (6:07:12)*

2013–up: men–Claude Moshiywa South Africa (5:32:09) women–Elena Nurgalieva Russia (6:27:09)*

2014–down: men–Bongmusa Mthembu S.A. (5:28:29) women–Eleanor Greenwood United Kingdom (6:18:12)*

2015–up: men–Gift Kelehehe S.A. (5:38:36) women–Caroline Wostmann S.A. (6:12:22)*

2016–down: men–David Gatebe S.A, (5:18:19) women–Charne Bosman S.A. (6:25:55)*

A Champion Chip is now used for recording each runner's unique link via the Comrades Marathon database. This chip was introduced in 1994 and is laced onto the runner' s shoe and records individual times on the route (via crossing timing mats and at the finish.

This ultramarathon has endured many technological and historical changes and grown and reshaped with the times. The Comrades Marathon is indeed, a living Memorial to human endurance and to the spirit of commitment. One can only wonder how many participants will run in 2021—100 years after its founding—and how many new records might be established.

Bibliographical Sources

Additional List of Winners 1921–1990

Check out www.comrades.com—excellent resource.

Books

Johannesburg One Hundred by Ellen Palestrant (A.D. Donker (PTY) LTD. 1986)

Have You Ever had a Hunch? The Importance of Creative Thinking by Ellen Palestrant. epCreative enterprises, 1994, 2005. 2014

Not Black, Not White The Politics of Apartheid in South Africa by Steve Farrah (New World African Press. 2007)

South African Historical Journal (20) Harry Phillips

The Boer War by Thomas Pakenham. London: Futura. 1982.

The Class of 1955 and I by Maurice Kahn, 2016. isakahn@gmail.com

Film

Sammy the Journey, documentary produced by Eric Cosh and Ellen Palestrant, 2014

Newspapers and Online Sources

The Star, 1920 onwards

Rand Daily Mail, 1903 -1985

www.longlongtrail.co.uk/

www.runnersworld.com

www.wow.com

www.news.comrades.com

www.sahistory.org.za

www.southafrica/info

www.comrades.comwww.runner.co.za/

www.runners.co.za

Some books on the Comrade Marathon you might want to read:

Runaway Comrade Bob de la Motte Quickfox Publishing

Comrades Marathon by John Cameron Dow Penguin books

The Comrades Marathon Story by Morris Alexander (1976)

Comradess Marathon Yearbook 1998 by Ian Laxton & Bruce Fordyce

Comrades Marathon Tom Cottrell

And there are many more…

45854531R00064

Made in the USA
San Bernardino, CA
01 August 2019